Natural Landscapes

Of The

Niagara Escarpment

Gun Point, Lions Head Peninsula.

NATURAL LANDSCAPES
OF THE
NIAGARA ESCARPMENT

PHOTOGRAPHY AND TEXT BY

RICHARD KOSYDAR

PUBLISHED BY

TIERCERON PRESS

Published in Canada by: Tierceron Press
                          76 Maple Avenue
                          Dundas, Ontario L9H 4W4
                          Telephone (905) 628-9092

Canadian Cataloguing in Publication Data

Kosydar, Richard
     Natural Landscapes of the Niagara Escarpment

ISBN 0-9694077-1-8

     1. Niagara Escarpment—Pictorial works.
2. Niagara Escarpment—Description and travel.
I.   Title

QH106.2.O5K68 1996   917.13   C96-900620-9

Printed in Canada by Friesens

Cover photo: Below Websters Falls in Spencer Gorge
Back Cover: Looking down from the cliffs at Lions Head

First Title Page: Niagara Falls (The American Falls)

Acknowledgments

I would like to thank the staff of the Niagara Escarpment Commission for their encouragement and support. Richard Murzin was his usual charming and sublime self; Sue Powell was a great help; David Wells, perhaps without knowing it, was the Godfather of this book; and Bob Pepper's comments on my maps kept them from being a disaster. The NEC library made my research much easier.

I have drawn heavily upon the Leading Edge Conference Proceedings for 1995 and 1996.

Marjorie Davison, now happily and busily retired, took the time to discuss her book *St. Vincent—The Tree with the Broken Branch* with me and to arrange a meeting with Rod MacAlpine. Major MacAlpine, now retired, was the Commanding Officer at the Tank Range while it underwent its recent large-scale renovations and he filled in many details on what has happened to the base over the years.

Ralph Krueger, a retired Geography Professor, was good enough to chat with me about the Escarpment. As a retirement project, he has created his own 25-acre botanical garden on his property just south of Thornbury.

I had always hoped to meet Dr. Walter Tovell after practically memorizing his great text, *Guide to the Geology of the Niagara Escarpment*, which is available from the NEC. I was able to enjoy his hospitality within the ambience of his home, which is a converted rural schoolhouse. I found his treed property to be a restful retreat.

John Koegler, a retired Geography teacher, takes commercial air photos under the name of Geovisuals. He took the excellent graphic of Cabot Head on the Bruce Peninsula. The NEC let me reproduce their copy.

My wife Eleanore, a poet and nature photographer, is a master at taking poetic photographs of water and rock. She took the photograph on page 10, along with the four pictures of Rockway Falls. She also contributed several other photographs of The Southern Scarp, edited the text, and helped to arrange the photographs. It is good to have this woman.

CONTENTS

Rock, moss and tree compositions of great beauty can be found anywhere on the talus slopes of the exposed scarp.

INTRODUCTION

The Niagara Escarpment is a landform of great beauty and amazing variety. It is an imposing geologic structure spanning hundreds of miles from New York state through Ontario to eastern Wisconsin. My objective in this book is to describe and illustrate, in a systematic fashion, the diversity of Escarpment landscapes in Ontario. Colour photographs and maps are used to bring the landscapes and anatomy of the Escarpment to life.

I wish to give the reader an easily grasped visual impression of the many faces of the Niagara Escarpment from the Bruce Peninsula to the Niagara Gorge. One can walk this length of Escarpment from end to end along the Bruce Trail. Automobile tours, although lacking the intimacy of experience that walking provides, allow one to enjoy the vistas.

I have divided the Escarpment into four main regions, which I feel most readily gives a quick grasp of the range and diversity of this impressive landform. The photographs have been grouped into these four regions so that the differences between areas will be more apparent, and one can readily gain a "feel" for each individual area. As the title of the book suggests, I have focused upon the landscapes of the Escarpment and have no individual portraits of the creatures or plants that live on it. It is the land that I wish to portray.

I have lived most of my life in the Hamilton area, in the presence of the Niagara Escarpment. For many years I thought that what I saw and experienced was pretty well what the rest of the Escarpment must be like—a series of limestone cliffs. I had been to Niagara Falls and it looked like a larger version of what we have in the Hamilton area. I had never seen any of the Escarpment north of Hamilton, but could not imagine it being different and felt no desire for further explorations. Not until I read two special books.

One is a beautiful coffee table book with superb photography by Pat and Rosemarie Keough. The other is a totally different but equally enjoyable text by Walter Tovell, now retired from the Royal Ontario Museum. Dr. Tovell's book describes and explains the geology of the Escarpment in an easily understandable fashion and was intended for classroom use. Both in their unique ways opened my eyes to the diversity of the Escarpment, and to a beauty that I had not realised was there.

This book is a direct result of these authors' efforts, and attempts to incorporate aspects from both of these fine works. It is intended for two different levels of interest. One is for the reader who will scan the book quickly; the other is for the reader who will have the interest and time to come back to it again.

Andy Warhol, one of America's better-known pop artists and philosophers, once said that in the age of television anyone could be famous for fifteen minutes. Having previously produced and marketed a coffee table book, it is my contention that such books are read for about fifteen minutes—especially if the pictures are pretty. Coffee table books are purchased primarily as thoughtful gifts. The purchaser skims through, thankful and relieved to have found a relevant and thoughtful gift. The recipient skims through, glancing at the photos, pleased to have received such a thoughtful gift. The book industry is pleased and relieved to have sold something.

I hope to leave those who have only a passing and limited interest in the Escarpment (or this book) with the impression of an unusually varied series of landscapes—landscapes that differ not only in appearance but also in terms of emotional feel. The marine cliffs of the relatively remote Bruce Peninsula, water lapping at their base, are a world apart from the cliffs of the Niagara Peninsula with a sea of houses or grape vines at their feet. Large areas of the Escarpment are covered by glacial debris, rocky cliffs nowhere to be seen. I have tried to give full representation to all these areas in the collection of photographs.

For the minority of readers with a greater interest in the Escarpment, I have produced a few maps that may be useful to look at from time to time. The written material differs from what is already available on the bookshelves mainly in presenting interpretative verbiage more concisely and in summarising recent research findings. My real challenge was to illustrate simply and graphically the varying physical structure of the Escarpment.

There are perhaps a greater number of broad, long-distance vistas among the photographs than is usual for a book of this type. This is especially the case in the middle portion of the Escarpment. While the long perspectives may lack the visual impact of more close-in photos, the vistas are an essential part of the Escarpment experience. They are what you see, what you get there; and as such I felt they should be included.

The map diagrams are intended as a means for readily expanding knowledge of the main physical features of the Escarpment. One of my personal goals was to be able to look at a map showing only an outline of the Niagara Escarpment and give a name to all the jogs and jags—such as, say, the Credit Valley and the Caledon and Albion Hills, which are followed by the Hockley Valley. What and where are the main valleys and uplands? Where are the "outliers" found? Such pursuits are perhaps not for the average reader. But for those with a greater interest in learning about the physiography of the Escarpment, the material presented here may be a useful reference. Why, you may ask, would anyone want to know such facts? That, dear reader, I leave to you.

As I drove around looking for photographs to take, I found the roads that criss-cross the Escarpment to be an experience in themselves. Several roads that looked respectable enough on a map turned into narrow, winding, steep single-lane paths that seemed little different from what the original pioneers carved out over a century ago. One minute I would be driving along the usual gravel farm road; then suddenly, farmland was replaced by trees or abandoned fields and a new little adventure would begin. Most of these "bush" sections of road on the steeper side of the Escarpment lasted only a few kilometres. To a gentle city boy like myself they were at first disconcerting, but after a while it occurred to me that if little old grannies could casually use roads like this on a daily basis then perhaps I would survive. My main fear was that at the most remote place they would be impassable and I would get stuck or have to back out a long way. After a while I came to enjoy driving on them since they are so pretty and peaceful. Such roads are found from one end of the Escarpment to the other.

I would like to mention two Escarpment roads that I found particularly interesting. At the upper end of the Beaver Valley is a commercial ski run. Running parallel to it is a road that goes straight up the valley wall with some hairpin turns near the top. After all my adventures on other steep roads, I felt like a hardened, machoed guy in possession of all the brain power that this genre of male is noted for. And so I went up this road. In places the road narrows and two vehicles cannot pass. But since so few vehicles use such a rugged road the odds are in your favour. I went up this road again another time and it did not seem as steep as the first time. But I still think the best way up that slope is on the ski lifts that parallel the road.

P.S. This road is not maintained in winter.

The other road was in Keppel Township just north of the hamlet of Kemble. The main road came to an end at a T-shaped corner, and traffic turned left or right. But a one-lane path freshly resurfaced with crushed stone went straight on. It was so narrow that two small cars could not pass without one going onto the adjacent field. Given the rigid grid system, I concluded that it was a public road and not an unmarked private laneway. This is not always self-evident, and on more than one occasion I have found myself on some private but unmarked farm drive where the drive was bigger and in better shape than the public road. Road layouts in rugged rural areas with few people are often less formal than in the more heavily populated areas. Anyway, it was most enjoyable driving on my own little path through farmers' fields and then descending to a step on the Scarp on a tight little hairpin turn. Not knowing what to expect adds interest to exploring these little byways; but they have their own inherent charm. I suspect that larger parts of the road system were like this until automobiles became common.

When the new lands were first surveyed in the 19th century, roads were laid out in a rigid grid pattern upon some very irregular topography. These concession or "farm" roads followed geometric lines on a piece of paper, and no one seemed to worry about the steep grades that the Escarpment face produced. It took virtually a vertical cliff or large swamp to stop or divert the pioneer road builders. In winter, a few of the steepest or most remote roads are posted with "No Winter Maintenance Beyond This Point" signs, but most are salted and sanded in their steepest portions, and life seems to go on. I spoke with an individual who lives near a hairpin turn on the Milton Outlier so tight that buses and large trucks are forbidden to use it. His response was that while the road is a little formidable at first, you soon get used to it, and there are relatively few periods when it cannot be used.

To me, these back roads seemed the last vestiges of an untouched rural Southern Ontario. It was a shock, therefore, to see huge monster houses suddenly appearing out in the middle of nowhere. Along with the rest of the province, the Escarpment anywhere near a city has rapidly been becoming "rural residential" for many years now. The picturesque nature of the Escarpment, the vistas that it affords, and its proximity to Toronto create a strong demand for building lots. After a while I came to expect huge residences any and everywhere. Some are tastefully and indeed discreetly done; others are of such architectural merit that only their owners and assessment-conscious municipal councillors can truly appreciate them.

The Escarpment lands have a distinctive "feel" to them. Driving systematically on the many roads that cross the Escarpment, I would be sometimes at its foot and other times on top of it. In many areas where the rock is broken and earth-covered, it is not at all obvious where the Scarp face itself begins and ends. The presence of a more wooded landscape, more rugged topography, and/or the appearance of vistas would often tell me that I was on the Escarpment itself. In some highly dissected areas where glacial debris covers the rock, a sense of enclosure was a distinguishing sign. A seasoned traveller of Escarpment lands eventually develops a sixth sense which tells him when he is into Escarpment terrain.

In general, the Escarpment is a green, rugged, linear island in a sea of gentler, more open farmland. In some areas it is a readily defined narrow band of green. In other areas, such as Mono or Mulmur townships where it is almost totally buried, it helps to have a bedrock geology map handy to locate it.

The pleasure that I experienced while taking the photographs for this book is what I will remember most about this project. I made numerous trips and on all of them had a feeling of exhilaration. Those were truly exquisite, halcyon days. I was enthralled by the sheer beauty of the ever-changing Escarpment lands that I traversed—like a young man captivated by a beautiful woman. It is full of enchanted places. On quiet, secluded Escarpment roads, it is possible to slow the car to a crawl or to take walks at one's leisure in the midst of incredible landscapes. It is, for me, less a place to study and more one in which to experience the loveliness of the countryside at its best.

The poetry of water and rock.

THE ESCARPMENT

The Bedrock

The Escarpment is the most visible and dramatic part of a larger geological structure known as a cuesta. A cuesta has a steep slope or scarp (an escarpment) on one side; and a long, gentle slope, often called the plateau or dip slope, on the other.

Roughly 400 to 450 million years ago, during the latter part of the Ordovician and the early and middle Silurian Periods, large areas of North America were covered by warm shallow seas. Materials deposited at the bottom of such seas would form the rocks of the Niagara Escarpment.

The depositional material came from two main sources: one inorganic and the other organic. Fine inorganic rock particles, such as clay and sand, were eroded from ancient mountain ranges in existence at that time. Organic material consisted of the remains of living creatures which populated the ancient seas. The marine creatures formed shells out of calcium dissolved in the sea water that was their home. Upon their demise, the calcium shells accumulated, and under the influence of pressure, heat and cementing solutions, were transformed into rock known as limestone.

In time, some of the limestone was altered by solutions carrying magnesium, becoming what we now call dolostone. Originally the term dolomite, familiar to an older generation, was used, but this term also refers to a mineral. To avoid confusion a new expression, "dolostone," was coined. Dolostone has the important property of being a hard and erosion-resistant rock—more so than the unaltered limestones.

Two kinds of marine creatures populated the shallow seas: ones that moved about in the water in a solitary fashion; and more social and sedentary creatures that formed colonies. When the solitary creatures died, their remains settled to the bottom of the sea, a little like snow falling to the ground. Over millions of years their shells and residues accumulated to form horizontal beds. If this "snowfall" was interrupted after a relatively brief period, thin beds would be created; and if allowed to continue over a long period, thick beds would result. It is these horizontal limestone beds that most of us are familiar with. I think of the Escarpment as being a tombstone, a horizontal monument to the countless little creatures that lived here so long ago.

A second, less familiar rock-producing mechanism was the formation of dome-shaped reefs by colonies of corals and calcareous algae, a process that still goes on today in warm tropical seas. One generation of corals would establish itself on the remains of its predecessors and the dome would slowly grow—a little like a skyscraper, where another floor is repeatedly added to the top of the last one built.

The ancient domed structures grew in height as water levels slowly rose in the ancient seas, since corals seek to remain near the surface of the water, where light, oxygen and nutrients are optimal. Rock formed from reefs lacks bedding planes and usually has a porous structure. The absence of clear fracture lines makes the rocks of reef origin more resistant to erosion than the bedded rocks. Dome building and the laying of horizontal beds went on simultaneously, and domes are embedded in the surrounding layers. Reef rock is sometimes hundreds of feet high. In the Bruce Peninsula it often forms the headlands which jut out into the Bay.

Two hundred and fifty million years can be, to paraphrase a popular expression, a long time in geologic history. This is how much time has passed since the ancient seas receded for the last time, exposing the strata they left behind to powerful earth movements and to the forces of erosion.

Movement deep within the earth's crust tilted and bent the flat rock. It is fairly common knowledge that tilting occurred, which in turn contributed to the formation of the scarp face. But a less known fact is that the Escarpment was bent into a gentle arch by the same forces that created the tilt. The middle portion of the Escarpment near the Blue Mountains in the Collingwood area is highest—about 550 metres above sea level. At Tobermory and Niagara Falls it is approximately 200 metres above sea level. This massive structural arch underlies most of Southern Ontario and is called the Algonquin Arch.

Two conditions must be present for an escarpment to form: the tilt of layered rock out of horizontal, plus interspersed layers of hard and soft rock. The simple mechanism of hard and soft rocks eroding at different rates has allowed the steep scarp of the Escarpment to develop. Soft shales rot and erode at a much faster rate than the harder dolostone above, creating such a large overhang that the undercut rock breaks away under its own great weight. The broken rock then tumbles down the brow, collecting at the foot of the cliff. This material is called talus. The size of rock masses that break away can be enormous. Some individual rocks in the Niagara Glen area of the Niagara Gorge are the size of two-storey houses.

The Escarpment can be thought of as a grey limestone giant with feet of clay—red clay. If it did not have feet of clay it would not be a giant. Queenston shale and the red clay that forms from it can be found in many places along the Escarpment from the Niagara Peninsula to the Cape Rich Foreland. It is at its most interesting and photogenic in the Credit River Valley just north of Cheltenham, where it forms a small area of badland topography composed of numerous gullied hillsides. Badlands are normally found in semi-arid climates, but thanks to these reddish clays banded with greyish-blue clays, we have our own badlands in this part of the world. Being a rare landform for the area has made them a bit of an attraction.

We saw how the limestone rock is made up of the last remains of tiny marine creatures, and hence is of biological origin. The shale was laid down as an ancient delta by mud-laden rivers that were breaking down and carrying away mountains found where the Appalachian Mountains are today. This is similar to the processes building the Mississippi or Nile River deltas today. Both these huge modern deltas are covered with a variety of plants. But the ancient deltas were barren mud flats stretching to the horizon. No, this was not because of the environmental policies of some unmentionable government. These fine materials were being laid down during the Ordovician Period—a time before plants on land had evolved, when life was still confined to the seas.

As I clambered about the Escarpment, I often found myself standing at the edge of a precipice atop a massive overhang, contemplating the fact that such structures have a limited life span. When I was not on top of an overhang, I was just as often standing underneath one contemplating the fact that they have a limited life span. Fortunately for scientific thought, Issac Newton did his contemplating under an apple tree.

The numerous layers or strata of shale, sandstone and limestone laid down by ancient, shallow, marine seas have been named by geologists. The stratification is rather complex, as the strata vary in thickness and in spatial distribution. I have found it possible to remember three layers which may be of interest to laymen: they are often mentioned on the bronze interpretative plaques found along the Escarpment.

At the top of the Escarpment is a layer of hard dolostone, called the Lockport Formation in the Niagara Gorge; it gradually merges with the Amabel Formation farther north. One authority for purposes of simplification refers to it as the Lockport-Amabel Formation in his text for students. This formation forms the principal caprock throughout much of the Escarpment. Another, lower dolostone known as the Manitoulin Formation forms a secondary scarp in the Georgian Bay area. A bottom layer called the Queenston Formation is composed of the soft red shale just spoken of.

The scarp face has been eroding back from where it originated. There is no way of telling where it started or how far it has retreated. Not only has the Escarpment as a whole been eroded back by the process of undercutting, but the much more rapid action of river erosion has cut valleys into its face, giving it a more irregular outline than is generally recognised. A glance at any of the maps will illustrate this irregularity.

Parts of the Escarpment have been cut off from the main scarp in its retreat. These islands of bedrock are known as outliers. River erosion is the usual mechanism by which they are formed. River valleys eroding far into the main plateau cut off a protruding part of the scarp in a pincer-like action reminiscent of a similar type of military manoeuvre. The outliers are quite varied. Some like the Milton Outlier are clearly defined. Others like the Caledon bulge are only partially cut off, while yet others have been totally buried by glacial debris and are known only to geologists.

The Legacy of the Glaciers

The appearance of the Escarpment would be profoundly different today if it had not been subject to glaciation. We have been discussing the bedrock geology of the Escarpment, that is, its rock foundation. Now we will look at how ice eroded this rock base and deposited materials on it.

The glaciers arrived one to two million years ago, and disappeared about 12,000 years ago. During this "Ice Age," more formally called the Pleistocene Period, massive sheets of ice several kilometres thick were centred over the Canadian Shield and covered most of Canada. Acting like giant rasps and conveyor belts they scoured the northerly areas beneath them and deposited much of this material at their more southerly snouts. It was a major exercise in earth moving and sculpting.

The entire Escarpment was glaciated, but the effects of glaciation vary dramatically from one region to another. The ice heavily scoured the Bruce Peninsula, leaving the limestone bedrock either completely exposed or with minimal soil covering. The middle portion of the Escarpment, by contrast, was mostly covered with glacial deposits, and few bedrock exposures can be found. In the southerly portion of the Escarpment a more even balance exists between exposed and covered rock scarp.

It is not generally realised that over half the Escarpment's face is covered by glacial deposits. Dramatic rock scarps are the dominant feature only in the Bruce Peninsula. Even the Blue Mountains, looming almost 300 metres above Nottawasaga Bay, are covered by a mantle of earth. Without this earth cover there would be no skiing on these steep scarps—just rock climbing, as in the Bruce.

The glaciers not only carried away soils and loose materials that had been created over many millions of years; they also broke down and carried away large amounts of bedrock and had the general effect of softening the appearance of the Escarpment. They widened, deepened and rounded the outlines of existing river valleys. The softened "U" shape of the Beaver Valley and the Nassagaweya Canyon are excellent examples of this aspect of glacial erosion. Exactly how much material the glaciers removed from the river valleys, and how much the pre-glacial rivers had eroded, is open to conjecture and will probably never be known. The largest valleys are too large for glaciers alone to have gouged out in the relatively short time of their active erosion, but well within the rivers' capabilities given the much greater time span they had to work in.

Along the edge of the Escarpment brow, glacial scour left bedrock near the surface in many locations. Swamps are often found in these areas of thin soil. The Kolapore and Rob Roy Swamps just a little southwest of Collingwood, as well as swamps in Caledon and Flamborough, are examples of such poorly drained areas that can be attributed to glacial action.

The Scarp as Habitat

An unusually wide variety of habitats is found on the Escarpment. They range from sun-beaten, drought-stricken bare rock to north-facing slopes that are perpetually moist, shaded and cool and composed of deep soft humus. Vertical rock walls and talus slopes exist beside spring-fed swamps. The ruggedness of the terrain and its unsuitability for agriculture has allowed native plants to survive here relatively free from human interference.

The very limestone rock itself attracts calciphiles, or calcium-loving plants. Wide variations in moisture, shade, temperatures and soils have produced a large number of specialised and often rare habitats. These in turn have allowed not only a large number of species to exist, but also a significant number of rare plants to find a home. Here we find 38 species of orchids, including the Showy Orchid and the Calypso. Rare ferns like Hart's-tongue and Walking Fern are among the 48 fern species found in these areas of the Escarpment.

It is the dramatic vertical rocky cliffs that give the Escarpment its public identity and probably its political raison d'etre. Yet until about ten years ago these rocky cliff faces had never been subjected to any long-term scientific study. After all, what was there to study on these barren cliffs? In 1985 the Cliff Ecology Research Group was formed at the University of Guelph to look more closely at the ecology of the rock face. One of their major areas of interest has been to study the eastern white cedars (Thuja occidentalis) that grow on the slopes from one end of the Escarpment to the other.

The existence of cedar trees on the Scarp face has been known for a long time. But what this Group has brought to light is the great age of these trees. By counting their annual growth rings and using radiocarbon dating, it has been learned that numbers of these cedars have life spans over 1650 years. Size is not an indicator of age. The oldest trees usually develop a gnarled, contorted, almost cork-screw appearance and can be quite small.

The cliffs are not monolithic surfaces, but have numerous cracks and ledges of varying size containing minimal amounts of soil. With time, various tree seeds land in these pockets and germinate. Only the young cedars survive; others like maple and ash that are dominant in normal woodlands die out on these marginal cliff sites. The cedars under such extreme environmental stress show some of the slowest rates of growth ever recorded. Studies have shown that water is not a factor limiting their growth. The layered and cracked nature of the rock allows water to slowly percolate to their roots. The exact limiting factors have not been established, but lack of nutrients such as phosphorus has been linked to reduced rates of growth in controlled experiments.

Experiments also indicate that these cedars have another interesting survival mechanism. It appears that each part of the root system is connected to a specific part of the upper tree, and if part of the root dies, only what is connected to that root is affected and the rest of the plant is able to carry on. This is a useful trait since it is not uncommon over a period of hundreds of years for some rock movement to occur that damages part of the root system.

The Cliff Ecology Group has postulated that similar ancient vertical forests exist in other parts of the world where stressful conditions and lack of interference by man and fire are found. Not long ago I read the following passage: "Except in the Virginia mountains, where Arbor-vitae clings to limestone ledges, this tree commonly inhabits swampy ground...". One suspects that these Arbor-vitae (another name for cedars) in the Virginia mountains also have life spans well beyond the normal time allocated to the eastern white cedar.

The bristlecone pine (Pinus aristata) grows in high, cold, rocky, wind-swept elevations in the mountains of the Southwest United States. It has been called a "gaunt runt." But it has been known to live for more than 4000 years. The oldest, called "Methuselah," is over 4700 years of age and is the oldest living thing on this earth.

Not only do the cliff cedars live to an ancient age, but their remains seem to last indefinitely. When the trees die, their roots eventually rot out and they fall to the talus slopes at the bottom of the cliffs. Here in these boulder-strewn environments they are above the damp soils, and any moisture is free to drain from them. Radiocarbon dating has established the age of some of this debris to be over 3000 years. Hikers have been known to use this wood for camp fires—wood that in some cases may have existed since the age of the Egyptian Pharaohs, giving new meaning to the expression "well-seasoned" firewood.

While these remnants seem old, even more ancient cedar trunks 9000 years of age exist. Their roots are still firmly anchored in the barren limestone bedrock. Few know of them and fewer still have seen them, for they are found on the rocky bottom of Georgian Bay. The level of Georgian Bay has fluctuated some hundreds of feet. At times it has been above current water levels and at times below this range. These fluctuations were mainly the result of changes brought about by glacial activity. During a low water period, parts of the Bay near the present shore were exposed, and here the cedar trees grew. Eventually, when the lake waters rose, they submerged the forests and embalmed the trunks in their frigid waters.

Historical Settlement

Let us look briefly at the historical settlement of the Escarpment. In the years before the industrial era, when water power was the principal source of energy, the early entrepreneurs were attracted by the streams that flowed near and over the Scarp face. Many mills were built that harnessed the power of the water rushing by. As a result, numerous small, economically viable and self-sufficient settlements developed along the Escarpment, especially in the valleys that the streams had carved out.

These rather isolated communities were serviced by wagons and stage coaches on primitive roads. The wagons took out produce—usually agricultural products such as wheat and woollen goods that had been supplied by local farmers and processed by the water-powered mills. Only more specialised goods that local tradesmen could not supply were brought in. The local artificers built those items most often needed, such as plows, equipment for horses, and domestic furniture. Until the introduction of mass-produced goods from industrial centres, these tradesmen were economically competitive. In time they were gradually supplanted by cheaper goods brought in from new factories in cities on the newly developed railways.

With the coming of steam power and railroads, only certain settlements on the railways, such as Orangeville and Collingwood, grew to become larger urban centres. With the coming of the automobile even the commercial activities of the hamlets declined, as people could easily travel to the cities to do their shopping. Much of the economic activity in the "less fortunate" communities withered away, and they became quiet backwaters. The historical pattern described above was typical of many rural communities and not just those on the Escarpment, although the more rugged topography there may have accelerated the process.

The waters flowing over the Escarpment quickly became the single most important source of energy for Ontario's hydro-electric industry, especially with the development of Niagara Falls. As early as 1898 DeCew Falls, just outside of St. Catharines, was used to generate electricity for transmission to Hamilton. A number of Escarpment mill owners, such as at Cataract in the Credit Gorge, converted their mills to electrical generation; they eventually went under or were bought out by Ontario Hydro as a provincial power grid was developed.

At the turn of the century private entrepreneurs showed interest in developing the power potential of Eugenia Falls which is in the upper end of the Beaver Valley. Ontario Hydro eventually took over the project and during the early years of World War I dams were built and the Beaver River Valley above the Escarpment was flooded, creating an artificial lake called Lake Eugenia. The water that flowed over Eugenia Falls was diverted by pipelines to a small power station a short distance away, reducing the Falls itself to a trickle.

Another early Escarpment resource use was the rock itself. Limestone was quarried for building stone and for the production of lime. Lime was created by burning the rock in special kilns, and was used primarily for masonry mortar, plaster and whitewash. Limehouse, in the valley of the Black Creek (a tributary of the Credit River), was a centre noted for lime kilns. Shale was used to make bricks, and brickyards were found along the entire length of the Escarpment. Today the ruins outside of Cheltenham are the most visible reminder of the era. Sandstone was also quarried, with the Credit Valley supplying stone for the Ontario Parliament Buildings in Toronto.

Actually, the earliest quarrying on the Escarpment took place some 11,000 to 12,000 years ago while the glaciers were still receding. This area was colonised at that time by Early Paleo-Indians who migrated from more southerly areas of the continent. They were hunters and gatherers who lived in small mobile bands and hunted caribou in a landscape that resembled today's Arctic in climate and vegetation. Archaeological researchers have been working on a site in the

Beaver Valley near Red Wing that was a source of chert for these early people. Chert is a hard shiny glass-like white rock composed of silica and is found in beds of limestone. It was used in the making of weapons and tools such as spear points and scrapers. The current thinking is that the Paleo-Indians returned to the site on a regular basis to restock their supply of this stone.

The early quarrying activities were small localised operations that had a minimal impact upon the Escarpment. It was not until the coming of the automobile and the crushed-rock or aggregate industry that quarrying had a major impact on the landscape. Today, from the air the southern Escarpment is literally the pits. Much of this activity is hidden from view by earth berms created around these huge holes in the ground.

When the newly emerging industrial centres were becoming economic dynamos, the Escarpment exerted its influence upon the location of transportation routes. We have all heard of the Great Wall of China. Well, another way to view the Escarpment is as the Great Wall of Southern Ontario. A wall at least one hundred metres high. Horse-drawn wagons were able to work their way slowly up a steep brow slope, as the road network laid out by the pioneers attests. But to a railroad, a steep slope is a significant obstacle; and finding a way up the Scarp was not always easy. The best gates through this wall are the river valleys that have much more gradual slopes up the Scarp face. These natural ramps are, even today, the location for railways and major roadways such as Highway 401.

The rugged Scarp face that hindered settlement in the early epoch of industrial development has now become a major attraction for the city dweller. Locations on the brow and on the picturesque slopes of the Escarpment command premium prices on the real estate market. Many of the small, charming Escarpment settlements within commuting distance are being developed as bedroom communities for the larger urban centres. It is only in areas as yet beyond the reach of the urban commuter that the untouched hamlets and countryside can be found.

Death and the Cliffs

Another aspect of the Escarpment is the ancient love lore of the native people. In these tales a common theme is that of young love foiled by the gods or tribal elders. A young chief of one tribe meets a forbidden maiden of another tribe and the two become romantically involved, with tragic consequences. In one story the two try to flee to find happiness but are pursed by wrathful elders. In imminent danger of being caught they seek refuge on forbidden Flowerpot Island. The gods, angered by this intrusion on their island, turn them into the two flowerpots. One is aware of the rocky road of true love, but this was a very hard way for the couple to end their days.

In another story, this one near the Blue Mountains, a young chief is killed for daring to seek the love of a certain young lady. The young maiden pines for her lost love and eventually dies of a broken heart in a suitably mystic Escarpment setting. In an age when women are too busy and stressed out with their careers to find much in the way of time or emotional energy to mourn the loss of a current intimate, one finds these tales rather charming.

An interesting rock formation looking down from the cliffs at Lions Head. The largest submerged rock has the appearance of an old sunken hull.

The Marine Scarp

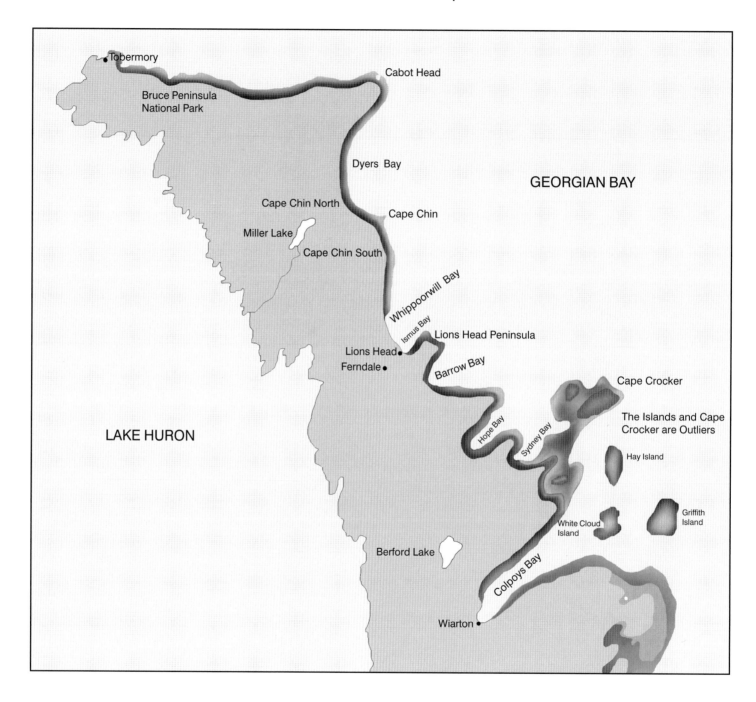

THE MARINE SCARP

The Bruce Peninsula is a land of rock and water. It is a narrow protrusion of limestone thrusting into the Great Lakes. On the eastern side of the Peninsula, a series of jutting headlands and bold cliffs overlooks a complex of bays and sounds. Inland, thinly covered bedrock with numerous rock exposures dominates the landscape. The bedrock, so high and proud as it overlooks Georgian Bay, gradually descends to the level of Lake Huron as it crosses the Peninsula to the west and quietly, inconspicuously but treacherously, disappears below its waters. The land is relatively flat, with only a few small hills (mainly in the Cape Chin area). Nowhere along the length of the Escarpment does the limestone bedrock play such a dominant role as in the Bruce Peninsula.

I consider The Bruce to be the area north of Wiarton. Others see it beginning at Owen Sound. Perhaps when you look at a map they are right. After all, the land mass narrows significantly at the latitude of Owen Sound. But for me, The Bruce is a region by virtue of its landscape: peninsular in nature and dominated by bedrock. This distinctive look and feeling only begins past Wiarton.

The glaciers were not kind to The Bruce. They took the soils that covered the land; scratched and grooved the rock; and left little in return. Only indirectly did the glaciers contribute to a mantle of good soil over a small part of the Peninsula, and that in their last dying gurgle. During the great melting of the glaciers, water levels of the surrounding lakes rose and covered some lower-lying regions. Around Ferndale, a glacial lake deposited a layer of clay that is the base of the only good agricultural soil in the upper Peninsula.

There is a core of thinkers who suggest that a massive deluge of flood water beneath the melting glacial ice further sculpted the land. Huge shallow sheets of water, flowing under the dying glaciers and originating hundreds of miles away, struck the Bruce Peninsula, creating forms that are typical of water erosion and not of ice action. Water-eroded features do not demonstrate the degree of rounding and smoothing that ice-sculpted forms do. There are channels or troughs tens of metres deep and hundreds of metres long that are best explained as features of water erosion. Where the water hit the scarp face itself, large potholes were created. Not only did Mother Nature scrub the Bruce Peninsula bare with glacial ice; the core thinkers tell us that she then rinsed it off with a glacial deluge.

The Bruce is a poorly drained land. It abounds in lakes and swamps. Looking below the surface of the shallow waters, bare rock can often be seen. A unique aspect of the Bruce not found elsewhere on the Escarpment is the absence of waterfalls of note on the main scarp. The Peninsula has the shape of a classic cuesta, and surface water is directed into Lake Huron following the gentle grade of the plateau. Only a small amount of surface water escapes the rocky grip of the cuesta, and it does so underground.

As hard and inviolable as dolostone may seem, it can be dissolved by water that is constantly in contact with it. Remember—this rock did not originate in the furnaces of the earth's depths; it was a gift of the warm tropical seas. What the waters give, the waters can take. Rainwater when combined with carbon dioxide or organic acids from vegetation forms a mild acid that can eat away at limestone. This can result in the pitting of rock surfaces, or in the creation of much larger features such as caves. The slightly acidic water makes its way through natural cracks in the bedrock, dissolving it to form underground passages. In a number of places, the water makes its way through subterranean watercourses to emerge as springs in the cliffs of Georgian Bay. Some inland lakes are drained by inconspicuous little openings in the ground.

If, perchance, our little heroine Alice had fallen into one of these openings, and not into a rabbit's lair, she would have found quite a different Wonderland. Had she shrunk to the size of a mouse she could have wandered through many miles of tiny tunnels dissolved out of the rock by groundwater. But we would hope she did her exploring when there was no chance of rain, because the tunnels could then easily flood.

The Escarpment has not developed the large limestone caverns that are found in the southern United States. In part, glacial activity disrupted the formation of karst features. The rock would have developed a deeply pitted surface and some enlarged openings prior to glaciation. But the glaciers with their icy fingers merely took advantage of these finger holds to grip and rip away all of this material, leaving the elements to start all over again on a clean slate. And it is a hard slate: dolostone dissolves at a slower rate than other limestones. Also, the layers of shale and clay, not being soluble, disrupt the cave building processes normally found in calcareous rock. So while there are solution caves in the Bruce, they are more limited in number and extent than what one would perhaps expect to find in limestone rock this old.

A cave that has aroused scientific interest was discovered fairly recently within the National Park area. Root Cave, as it is called, possesses such features as stalactites and stalagmites, suggesting that it was formed before the latest glacial period.

A distinctive kind of ecological community has developed in some places on the thinly covered limestone bedrock of the Bruce. A certain type of clearing, not created by natural fires or by human intervention, sometimes occurs where bedrock conditions are so harsh that normal tree growth has not taken place. In these openings grow stunted and deformed eastern white cedars hundreds of years old, typical of those found on the steep scarps. Centuries-old deadwood found alongside these ancient trees suggests that fires have not been active for long periods. These areas of level rock have been called "horizontal cliff faces."

The term "alvar" is used by botanists for these openings in the forests. An alvar has three components. First, the "ground" must be a limestone or dolostone bedrock. Second, the area involved must be generally open (not much in the way of trees), and thirdly, it must have some low vegetation (it can't be totally barren). Surprisingly, such areas are rare in the world. In Canada they are found only in Southern Ontario on the Bruce, on Manitoulin Island, and at the edge of the Canadian Shield where similar Silurian limestone outcroppings occur. Naturally occurring alvars do exist, such as the ones on the Bruce, but the majority are man-made ones.

The environment of an alvar is a harsh one, where only the hardiest of species can survive. Dolostone bedrock is normally grey, but the alvars have a blackish colouring to them due to algae that coat the rock surface. Lichens and mosses populate the bedrock. Tough grasses and wildflowers find minuscule pockets of soil to call home. In larger pockets of soil, dwarf cedar and tamarack trees establish roots. A special appeal of alvars to biologists is that they are home to numbers of rare plants such as the Lakeside Daisy.

The Escarpment continues underwater beyond the tip of the Peninsula. The shallow portion has been deadly to maritime traffic; the deep portion is more benign. To gain access to the wealth on Georgian Bay's shores, all vessels had to cross the area of shallow water, shoals and islands between Lake Huron and Georgian Bay. In the days before sophisticated navigation equipment and powerful dependable engines, the mariners of old were much more vulnerable to the dangers of the shoals just below the surface of the water. The distances that vessels have to travel are not great, but storms come up quickly and with a power and ferocity that can easily direct a vessel onto the rocks. These storms must be experienced to be believed.

The skies of the Bruce have an unusual and often dramatic beauty to them. Two large bodies of water surrounding a narrow peninsula creates a natural stage, over which the heavens paint an ever-changing canvas of clouds and light. In this essentially marine environment, atmospheric conditions are complicated by the sliver of land with temperatures that differ from that of the water. The result is a sky often covered by spectacular cloud formations lit by theatrical lighting, with gold and turquoise as common hues. Because the land is so flat, early morning and late evening sun can slip beneath the clouds, lighting them from below with their softest and richest light. All skies have their moments of glory, but these moments come more often to the skies of the Bruce.

Historically the Bruce was seen as a remote wilderness to be exploited with little concern for the future. Its two main resources, forests and fisheries, were quickly cleaned out at the end of the last century. The waste from forest cuttings led to some huge fires, which burned out large areas. It must have been quite an experience to travel through these barren and blackened areas in the early years of this century.

Today the Bruce is green again. Although large areas are wooded, one rarely finds any good-sized trees in areas not protected by government parks. My impression is that the great bulk of the woodlots are used as a source of firewood and the trees are cut down before too much, if any, splitting is required. A distinctive feature of the Peninsula's landscapes is the abundance of cedar trees. Elsewhere, cedar trees tend to be confined to and are diagnostic of swampy areas or the scarp face, while in the Bruce they are much more widespread and add a rich dark green accent to the countryside. Other common evergreens are spruce and balsam fir. The water-loving birches, along with aspens and the ubiquitous sugar maple, are the main deciduous trees.

The only significant good farmland of the Bruce is found in the Ferndale Flats. Pioneers drained low-lying swamps consisting of good clay loam by making ditches. A technique often used was to set in long rows of dynamite and blast the earth out.

Beyond this small area of good farmland, farms on shallow and rocky soils are scattered throughout the Peninsula. Here beef cattle graze, often amid boulders and bedrock outcroppings, in level to gently rolling fields enclosed by nearby woodlots. On fields more hospitable to machinery, hay is grown. The Bruce's farms never produced the wealth that the better soils and warmer climates did farther south, and as a result, farm houses and buildings are more modest than those found elsewhere.

Now the Bruce's source of wealth is tourists, cottagers and increasingly, retirees, who form colonies along both shores. On the Georgian Bay side, these colonies cluster in such bays as Dyers, Barrow and Hope and consist of dwellings packed as close to one another as is possible. I found the town of Lions Head to be the classiest of these communities. Perhaps it will become a Mecca for a generation no longer as young as it once was, whose professional days will soon be coming to an end, and whose hopes for upward mobility will of necessity be directed towards heaven.

Looking north across Colpoys Bay from Big Bay. The most southerly scarps of the Bruce recede into the distance.

Cabot Head from the air.

Zen-like rocks in grey light. The quiet stillness of the evening creates a meditative mood in the Bruce Peninsula National Park. Talus rock has accumulated at the base of the headland.

Massive rock overhang in the Bruce Peninsula National Park. The overhang was created by wave action at the end of the glacial period when water levels were much higher than today. These overhangs can be reached by wandering a little off the Bruce Trail in search of vistas. Usually you do not know you are on one until you have explored the edge a little. Shallow but large abandoned cave openings are also found at similar elevations above the current lake level. These, too, were carved out at the end of the glacial period by waves finding weaknesses in the layered rock. The best known of these glacial relicts is Bruce's Cave in Keppel Township. Similar undercutting and cave-building activity is taking place today at the present water level.

Portrait of a reef rock on Flowerpot Island. This unbedded boulder has fallen off the top of the Scarp brow and landed on clearly layered beds called limestone or dolostone *pavement.* The reef rock was formed by ancient coral reefs which were similar to coral reefs found in todays oceans. The level bedded rock was formed from the accumulated remains of individual small organisms; sinking to the bottom of the oceans, they were eventually transformed into solid rock. The reef rock, lacking bedding planes, is more resistant to erosion and often forms headlands and overhangs.

The Flowerpots. Created by wave action after the glacial period, these stone sculptures have been prevented from eroding away only with human help. The top has been capped by concrete and the undercut base bolstered with rock masonry infilling, as a careful look at the photograph shows. The cedar trees growing out of layers in the rock provide a nice aesthetic touch. While these two pots are the only fully-developed rock stacks, a series of embryonic ones still await release from the surrounding rock— a little like a figure in the middle stages of a Michelangelo sculpture. The structure of the rock formations in this area of Flowerpot Island renders them particularly susceptible to this type of wave sculpting.

Morning light on a swamp in the Cape Chin area. The low morning or evening sun often slips through little openings in the cloud cover and lights the land in a beautiful fashion. I suspect that the nature of its cloud cover allows this to happen more often in the Bruce than elsewhere.

Farmland in the Barrow Bay area in the early morning. These fields are a little larger and the soils less rocky than is typical of farms in the Bruce, but the sense of enclosure by forested land is still present. Once away from the coast there are no great vistas. The flatness and heavily-wooded nature of the land preclude this.

Terraced cobble beach in the Bruce Peninsula National Park. Angular bedrock materials were smoothed out, sorted and deposited by wave action. The terracing indicates that this activity took place at differing water levels. The highest terraces are well above the highest water levels of the beach today. One researcher suggests that the upper levels were formed about 3500 years ago when the level of the lake was somewhat higher. Cognoscenti will recognize this area as the Marr Lake Beach and remember the fun of walking on these cobbles.

Barrow Bay. Nestled into settings such as this along the coast of the Bruce Peninsula are numbers of cottage colonies. The building in this picture is unusually well-done architecturally, and blends in with the landscape very well. Usually the cottages are packed closely together.

Swamps are common and often very beautiful on the rock pavements of the Bruce. They are a product of the disrupted drainage left behind by the glaciers.

Promontory off Lions Head. A cedar stump holds out its dead limb to the light of the setting sun. There are endless variations on the theme of rock, cedars and water below. Often, to get a good picture at the cliff's edge you have to lean out over the precipice as far as you dare, keeping in mind that only one such fall is allotted to you in this life.

A typical sight from the Bruce Trail in the Bruce Peninsula National Park. This is an area very commonly visited by tourists, and it affords the opportunity for families to not only enjoy the scenery but also clamber around the rocks in comparative safety.

Evening sky over Ferndale Flats after a rainstorm. The long narrow land mass of the Bruce Peninsula is almost totally surrounded by water, a condition which often results in dramatic skyscapes. Notice how level the land is here.

Looking across Whippoorwill Bay to White Bluff near Lions Head. Throughout much of the Peninsula the bluffs run along the shoreline.

These rocks on Flowerpot Island evoke a feeling of the overgrown ruins of an ancient Greek amphitheatre. Note the fairly large cedar growing out of a layer in the rock.

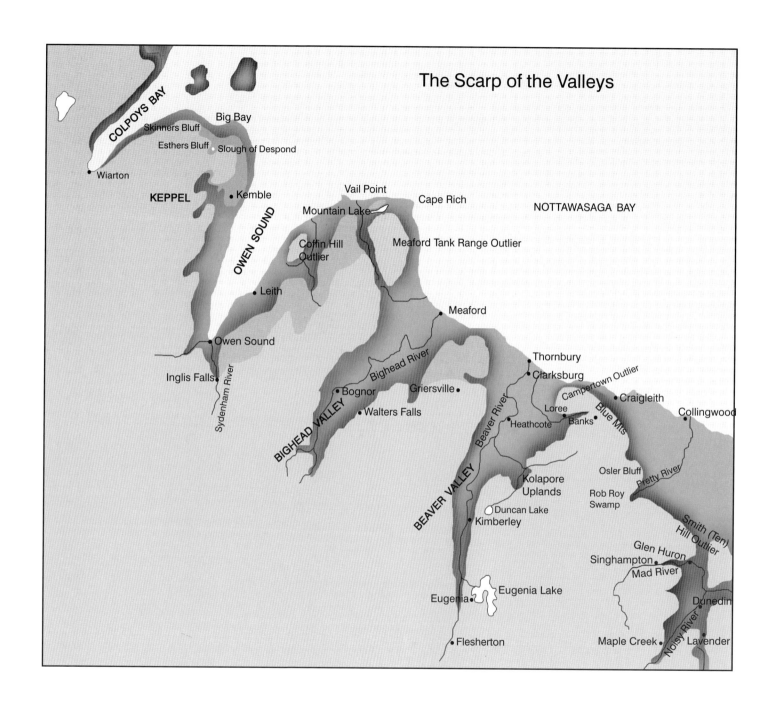

The Scarp of the Valleys

COLPOYS BAY

Big Bay

Skinners Bluff

Esthers Bluff • ○ Slough of Despond

Wiarton •

KEPPEL

• Kemble

Vail Point

Mountain Lake ◦ Cape Rich NOTTAWASAGA BAY

OWEN SOUND

Coffin Hill
Outlier

Meaford Tank Range Outlier

• Leith

• Meaford

• Owen Sound

Inglis Falls •

Sydenham River

Bighead River

Thornbury •
Clarksburg •

Campertown Outlier

• Bognor Griersville •

Beaver River

• Craigleith

Loree
•

Collingwood

• Walters Falls

Heathcote • Banks •

Blue Mts

BIGHEAD VALLEY

Kolapore
Uplands

Osler Bluff Pretty River

BEAVER VALLEY

○ Duncan Lake
• Kimberley

Rob Roy
Swamp

Smith (Ten)
Hill Outlier

Glen Huron

Singhampton • • Mad River

Dunedin

Eugenia • Eugenia Lake

• Flesherton

Maple Creek • Noisy River Lavender

38

THE SCARP OF THE VALLEYS

The Scarp of the Valleys is a region where four large valleys intrude into and break up the line of the Escarpment. All open onto either Georgian or Nottawasaga Bay. The two westerly valleys, Colpoys Bay and Owen Sound, lie underwater. The easterly valleys are named the Bighead and the Beaver, after the principal rivers that flow through them. All four valleys existed prior to the coming of the glaciers, but the ice deepened and smoothed their contours. Colpoys Bay and Owen Sound were deepened below the current levels of Georgian Bay. When the glaciers melted, lake water filled the bottoms of these drowned valleys.

The Scarp on its journey south from the tip of the Bruce Peninsula is the constant companion of Georgian Bay as far as Wiarton. Past this community, it swings slightly inland, and the magnificent coastal cliffs typical of the Bruce are no more.

The land between Wiarton and Owen Sound is a transition between the harsh rock of the Bruce and the kinder, gentler soils of the South. The rock does not let go without a struggle. The Escarpment now passes through Keppel Township, which is called "Stony Keppel" by the people who live there. As in the Bruce, there are areas of bare rock, boulder-strewn fields and swamps; but in general the soils are a little deeper and more plentiful, and the trees are taller.

The Escarpment has numerous sinuous indentations in this area. Nestled in one of these nooks and overlooked by Esther's Bluff is a little pond surrounded by a swamp. Delightfully named the Slough of Despond, the swamp is one of the ecologically significant areas for which the Escarpment is noted. You may get stuck in mud when walking through it, but do not confuse it with getting mired in the slough of despair. That depression is a lot harder to get out of.

A highly dissected promontory known as the Cape Rich Foreland or the Cape Rich Steps separates the waters of Owen Sound from the drumlins of the Bighead Valley. It has the usual geological profile for this area. Capping the foreland is the dolostone of the Amabel formation. Partway down, dolostones of the Manitoulin Formation form the base of a plateau. Between and below these two layers of hard rock are broad slopes of soft reddish shale. Near the shoreline are terraces cut into the shale by glacial lakes. Rivers cutting into the rock have produced rugged terrain and isolated a number of outliers. During World War II, part of this area was taken by the Military for use principally as a tank gunnery range.

Although the Tank Range is an interesting part of the Escarpment it is rarely mentioned in the historical literature, and so I am devoting more than my usual space to its story. In my readings I came across a book entitled *St. Vincent— The Tree with the Broken Branch*, by a local lady named Marjorie Davison. St. Vincent is the main township of the Bighead Valley and at one time encompassed a significant portion of the Cape Rich Foreland. In part of this book she chronicled the military take-over of the Tank Range during the War and its effects on the local people.

With the rapid growth of tank warfare in World War II the Army decided it needed a base where it could train its soldiers for armoured fighting. The Cape Rich area was chosen for two main reasons. One was its location beside a large body of water, namely Nottawasaga Bay. By cordoning off parts of the Bay adjacent to the Range when gunnery practices were underway, a large buffer area could be provided at minimal cost. Stray rounds would land harmlessly in the water. Secondly, the rugged terrain of the Scarp was ideal for gunnery safety and training required by the military.

One hundred farms totalling about 17,500 acres were expropriated to serve the Army's needs. This was an era when people did not travel as much as they do today; when telephone use was mainly local and there was no television. As a result, people's worlds were much smaller than now. Many of the people living on the future base were descendants of the original pioneer homesteaders, with family ownership dating back almost a century. This land was their home, and their lives were deeply woven into the social fabric of the local rural communities. For most, their land would also hold their graves. It came as a heartbreaking shock to learn that their farms had been expropriated and they had six weeks to get off the land.

The actual relocation was about as humane as the human condition allows under such rushed circumstances. The farmers were duly compensated for their land. But there were not enough farms in the local area to absorb all who wished to remain, and local land prices rose to reflect the sudden increase in demand. A fair market price for a few farms may not be quite as fair a market price when many farms are expropriated. One source of lingering disillusionment and bitterness, Mrs. Davison points out, was the impression given by government officials that as soon as the War ended the land would be returned to the original owners. One farmer had his barn reroofed in the six weeks given to him, expecting to be back before many years had passed.

With the compensation they received, the former landowners could buy other farms or go to the cities and find work in the booming war-time economy. But most of the mature generation were deeply affected by this forced expulsion, and the scars stayed with many for the rest of their days. This exodus from their farms may not have been of the magnitude or harshness of many other expulsions but it still produced a great deal of trauma and hardship: people with a close tie to the land had lost their homes. The initial and lingering pain for that generation was, I think, the message of Mrs. Davison's book.

The Army promised to tend the graves of those buried there, and it still does. Only those with relatives in the graveyard were allowed back onto the Range to visit the graves. It was not until 1984, the year of Ontario's Bicentennial Celebration, that the Military allowed the public at large to visit the Range. The local council requested permission to host a community reunion on the base and this permission was given. For the old generation that had felt the expulsion most acutely it was an emotional time. For their children the emotions were there but to a lesser degree. And for the generation of youngsters who had never known the area to be anything but a military base it was a great time. As they say: time and death are great healers.

The Armoured Corps used the range for training purposes until 1970. At that time they moved onto the much larger base at Gagetown in the Maritimes. The Meaford Range is sufficiently small in area that high-speed, large-scale manoeuvres using powerful weapons are not possible there. The army decided to pack up their big toys and go where they could run around and blast away to their heart's content. The large bases that will accommodate these activities are found on the Prairies or in the Maritimes; one is also located north of Ottawa.

The Meaford Range was mothballed for almost two decades, with only informal use by militia units. There was talk of returning it to civilian control but the cost of cleaning up the live ammunition on the practice ranges would have been very high. Probably of greater importance was the concern with finding replacement facilities if they should ever be needed. Nothing came of the initiatives.

In the late 1980s the regular army was down-sized and a greater emphasis was placed on the militia. The militia is by nature a weekend army devoting its weekdays to work or school. This meant that military training activities had to take place near the large population centres because of transportation considerations. The large concentration of people around the Great Lakes and Southern Ontario in general made it desirable to have a practice range nearby within weekend commuting distance. Meaford was the best alternative.

In the early 1990s facilities were greatly upgraded (to the tune of 100 million dollars) and now facilities exist for around 4,000 soldiers to live and train there. The Army has not only upgraded its physical facilities but has gone out of its way to minimise friction with the local people. But firing guns is still a noisy business, and especially on weekends, local residents around the base are treated to the cacophony of the big guns. It is an earth-moving experience listening to these guns—houses shake slightly from the concussions. The Army has minimised night-time firing. When there is to be range practice, patrol vessels scoot any boats that are in the restricted area out of harm's way. Today this area is two kilometres off shore. During the war, heavier guns were fired and a distance of ten kilometres was maintained.

Large parts of the base are not used by the military except as a buffer and have reverted back to forest, becoming a haven for wildlife and plants. Scientists who have been allowed onto the base have been encouraged by their findings. It is also perhaps not too surprising to learn that deer have multiplied and that they wander off the base and into nearby apple orchards. Balancing the needs of wildlife, agriculturists and local hunters has been a delicate balancing act.

The Bighead Valley is known for its distinctive streamlined hills, each having a characteristic steep and a gentle slope. These oval hills, called drumlins, were sculpted beneath moving glacial ice. They are social creatures and are often found clustered in large fields. There are about 300 of them in this valley, and they are found not only on the valley floor but also on its sides.

The Bighead and Beaver Valleys are separated by a protrusion of Escarpment known as the Griersville Rock. This promontory or narrow plateau gradually diminishes in height toward the North, and near the shore of Nottawasaga Bay it disappears completely. Interestingly, the Beaver Valley has only a few drumlins and they can be counted on one hand, even though no significant barrier lies between it and the Bighead Valley, which is plastered with these picturesque hills.

The Beaver Valley has two distinct parts. One is the dramatic U-shaped section of its upper, southerly portion and is what we usually see in photographs of the Valley. The larger, northerly section is broad and more gentle in relief. To the east the Valley is bordered by one end of the Blue Mountains and the slopes of the Kolapore Uplands. Many parts of the Uplands have shallow and rock-strewn soils, and have been reforested after attempts at agriculture proved futile.

General farming is practised in both valleys, with the emphasis on beef cattle. But the area is also the largest single apple-growing region in Southern Ontario. Both valleys have apple orchards near the tempering influence of Nottawasaga Bay, although the industry is larger in the Beaver Valley. The cold waters of the Bay keep the air cool in the spring and delay the blossoms a week or more, lessening the chance of a damaging spring frost that would kill the delicate blossoms. The blossoms come out later near the lake than farther inland.

The Bighead and Beaver Valleys have shown us grand vistas of lowlands with orchards and farms. We have seen the intervening and bordering highlands, with their pastures and woodlots. And unless we were some distance inland, the rich greenish blue of the inland seas have enriched these vistas.

Next on its journey toward Niagara, the Escarpment takes another sharp turn to begin its long southerly run. Anchoring this turn are the mighty Blue Mountains, the best-known of the Escarpment's ski areas. This is one of Toronto's playgrounds, reflected in the wall-to-wall ski runs down the massive bluffs, and in the newer residential architecture—both condos and private homes—around Collingwood. Owen Sound, on the other hand, is not a direct part of the Greater Toronto Area. Its buildings and lifestyle have more the feel of a small town, reflecting the ties to the farming community that it serves.

I have not tried to define a clear-cut boundary between the Scarp of the Valleys and the Earthen Scarp. I guess when you can no longer see the blue of Nottawasaga Bay, one region ends and the other begins. Such a definition may not impress Geography professors, but how many copies of this book will they buy? Somewhere between the Pretty River and the Mad River, the power of Georgian Bay is lost and we turn toward the inland valleys and uplands of the Niagara Escarpment.

The Escarpment near Esthers Bluff and Skinners Bluff. This area possesses panoramic views and sites of ecological importance. During the past year, the Bruce Trail Association purchased a key property near here which is an important link in its trail system. The Association has defined an optimal route along the Escarpment and is pursuing, with the help of a most earnest staff, access to this route. The B.T.A. is beginning to see itself as a land trust and has become a landowner of note along the Escarpment. Much of the Trail lies on private land, with access in the form of impermanent verbal agreements. With limited funding available, the B.T.A. is in the process of developing imaginative techniques with which to gain secure access to the lands they are after. One technique is to purchase a property, sever part of it for the trail corridor and then resell the remainder.

The eastern mouth of the Beaver Valley looking west from Banks. Here we are just beyond the steep ski slopes of the Blue Mountains, and the Escarpment has suddenly become very gentle. The waters of the bay add a rich blue accent to the landscape. This part of the Beaver Valley is the least seen and recognized by the outside world, which is more familiar with the Valley's more dramatic southern part. And even at that, the Beaver Valley is not particularly well known. Everyone has heard of Collingwood and the Blue Mountains, but that's about it. And how many decent, self-repecting Canadians have heard of the Bighead Valley?

Drumlins in the upper Bighead Valley well south of Meaford. This is an area with a pleasant mixture of woodlands and open fields. One minute you are in an intimate wooded lowland, and the next on top of a drumlin with a broad panoramic view.

An informal path near Indian Falls just north of Owen Sound. Often these paths are rugged and you have to exercise care when using them, but they can be quite interesting to explore. The development of casual paths along the Scarp face is common from one end of the Escarpment to the other and is probably the result of the activities of small numbers of young people over the centuries. Note the U shape of the cedar trunk and its loose dead roots.

Tributary of the Bighead River. Not all the drumlins are large-scale features. Although not well shown in the picture, even the more gently undulating hills have a streamlined drumlin-like line. This is salmon and rainbow trout country, and the Bighead is a major spawning river.

Mouth of the Beaver Valley near Nottawasaga Bay looking west. The Griersville promontory in the foreground slope separates the Beaver from the Bighead Valley. In the distance lies the Cape Rich Foreland. The Escarpment in this area is most notable for the long distance vistas which it makes possible. Here there are no magnificent bluffs, but the Alfred Hitchcock-like visage of the Scarp is everywhere to be seen.

Southern slope of the Bighead Valley. The drumlinoidal shaping of the land is still present. The greater number of woodlots at the top indicates the proximity of the Escarpment's brow, with its thinner and rockier soils. The white frame farmhouse is typical of the architecture of rural dwellings in this valley.

Late winter in the Bighead Valley. The basic form of the drumlin makes it a photogenic feature throughout the year.

Looking east across the waters of Owen Sound from the Escarpment in north Keppel. Just below is an Escarpment terrace or step formed on the Manitoulin dolostone. Not all of Keppel is overrun with rocks.

The legacy of the glaciers in Keppel Township near Zion. These large rocks give some idea of the power of glacial ice to grip and carry away limestone bedrock. I would imagine, dramatic though this picture is, and how well it illustrates my thesis of glacial activity, that some of the boulders were brought here from adjacent fields by farmers, since the surrounding area of cleared farmland is free of such impediments to farming.

The trees in the background are mostly sugar maples. Acer saccharum is the dominant species in Grey County, and almost pure stands are common. The smooth, light grey bark of the young trees creates a distinctive and beautiful effect.

Part of the Rob Roy swamp. This wetland near the Escarpment is the result of glacial activity that scoured the bedrock, leaving areas of poor drainage. Besides being a home for wildlife, the swamps help recharge the groundwater. One purveyor of bottled water pumps his water from deep wells close by. He comments, in private, that his pure water is filtered by the remains of creatures that have been dead for almost half a billion years.

Old Baldy outcropping in the upper Beaver Valley. Near and on the exposed rock, cedars are the dominant tree species. The now dormant sugar maples assume that role farther away from bedrock, where the soil is deeper. The farmland is gradually being abandoned.

The Sydenham River at Inglis Falls near Owen Sound during spring runoff. In sections where the Escarpment is covered by glacial drift, often the bedrock can be seen only in river valleys.

I tried to take a photo of the Falls itself but could not do so. There is only one vantage point that permits a good composition, but the sightlines were sufficiently overgrown that nothing more than a "Ma and Pa with the kids at the falls" snapshot would have been possible. Numbers of conservation authorities create, at great expense, first-class observation areas overlooking prize views and then allow the vegetation to obscure the view.

Fields, maple woodlots and promontories in Keppel Township. The Escarpment snakes its way between Wiarton and Owen Sound, creating many beautiful vistas that are not well-known. This photo was taken from an abandoned field full of rocks on top of almost barren bedrock. The ground was cracked and pitted—a fine example of karst topography. While there is a sense here of bucolic bliss amidst an arcadian landscape, I had the feeling that septic beds must be expensive to put in. A lot of crushed stone or gravel must be trucked in to make a safe septic bed. In this landscape of layered and cracked rock, not much separates one man's waste from his neighbours' drinking water even if they are some distance away.

Apple orchard in the Beaver Valley near Loree south of Thornbury. The sloping land facilitates air and water drainage, and although the soils here are heavier than the sandy loams that are generally considered optimal, high quality apples are grown. Notice that the orchards do not extend much higher. Subtle changes in soils and microclimates can make the line dividing economically viable orchard land from land that is unsuited for commercial production quite sharp. Northern Spies and Ida Reds are picked in mid- and late October, and there can be snow on the ground in years of early snowfall. In some years the snow is too deep to pick up the windfalls.

During spring and summer, the Bighead Valley glows with a green sheen. Most of the orchards in this valley are found on the flatter lake plain nearer the moderating influence of Nottawasaga Bay. A number, however, like the one to the right in this picture, are located in the middle of the valley on the slopes of the drumlins. Inland, good air drainage is especially important, to minimize the chances of frost damage from late spring frost since the blossoms come out a little earlier than near the cold lake.

The Beaver Valley at the edge of the Kolapore Uplands. Outcroppings of Escarpment rock can be seen in the distance. These are small resistant outliers left behind the retreating Scarp face.

Face of a small outlier at the edge of the Kolapore Uplands. Crevasses commonly develop when part of the rock face breaks off from the main body of rock. Rock movement is often facilitated by slippage when the layer of rotted shale and clay upon which harder limestones rest grows wet. Commonly, the narrow isolated rock strip will tumble back onto the main rock face. These crevasses at times are sufficiently enclosed to form what is called a crevasse cave.

The Bognor Marsh along the edge of the Escarpment in the Bighead Valley.

View from a large drumlin looking north toward Cape Rich. Numbers of farmers in the Bighead valley have located their homes on top of drumlins and have beautiful panoramic views.

The Upper Beaver Valley in late winter. The actual valley notch and its slopes are hidden from view. The upper levels are actively farmed, while the steeper slopes are almost all out of production. The smooth rounded look of the landscape reflects the glacial scouring that took place. The broad sweep of the landscape makes interesting lighting conditions possible. The far side of the valley is in deep shade while the near side is brightly lit.

Looking south across Colpoys Bay. This photograph illustrates the multiple scarps which have formed in this area. Amabel dolostone is the hard resistant cap layer at the top the Escarpment. The resistant layer at the lower level is Manitoulin dolostone. The slopes are composed of soft shales. Note the talus that has accumulated at the bottom of the upper slope. In the distance the islands found at the mouth of the bay can be seen.

The Earthen Scarp

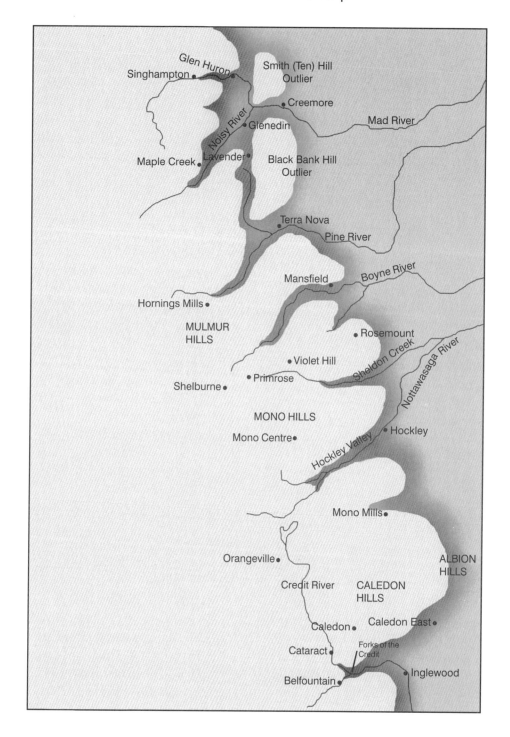

Glen Huron
Singhampton
Smith (Ten) Hill Outlier
Creemore
Mad River
Noisy River
Glenedin
Maple Creek
Lavender
Black Bank Hill Outlier
Terra Nova
Pine River
Mansfield
Boyne River
Hornings Mills
MULMUR HILLS
Rosemount
Sheldon Creek
Nottawasaga River
Violet Hill
Shelburne
Primrose
MONO HILLS
Mono Centre
Hockley
Hockley Valley
Mono Mills
Orangeville
ALBION HILLS
Credit River
CALEDON HILLS
Caledon East
Caledon
Forks of the Credit
Cataract
Belfountain
Inglewood

THE EARTHEN SCARP

Glaciers are very effective earth movers: they can move a lot of dirt in a hurry. Among the glacial period's most significant effects was the enormous transfer of material from North to South. The Northland was ravaged by ice that ripped and carried away its earthen mantle. Mother Nature's version of the Cold War, so to speak. The Earthen Scarp to which we now turn was a major recipient of the spoils of this war.

Along this portion of the Niagara Escarpment, most of the Scarp face is buried beneath large amounts of glacial debris. Here the ice front stagnated. Although the front was stationary, the ice mass itself continued to move (like a conveyor belt) and to melt, bringing with it enormous amounts of material and generating huge amounts of meltwater. Deposits laid down by this process are called moraines.

I think it may not be difficult for people to become "ho hum" over the topic of moraines. Not so for me. As I look upon them, I see not "glacial debris" but curvaceous objects draped over hard, angular bedrock. For our piddling life spans this is truly an eternal embrace. But being geological creatures they must live in geological time. And in terms of geological time this is but a short fling that will soon be washed up or, to be more precise, washed away as the forces of erosion gradually take away their substance. To me, this approach is much more enjoyable, if less useful, than the explanations given by geologists.

The thickness of glacial deposits along the Earthen Scarp varies greatly. Normally, the morainic material covers the rock face but leaves the outline of the underlying rock structure visible. The Blue Mountains are a particularly well-known example of this. However, in some places the Escarpment silhouette disappears completely. In the area between the communities of Primrose and Violet Hill (along Highway 89), the Scarp is nowhere to be seen. To get my photographs of this portion of the Escarpment, I went to the east of the buried edge of the brow, to Airport Road where there is a more Escarpment-like setting.

While the limestone bedrock is almost completely buried in this area, there are a few places where it appears. The best known is in Mono Provincial Park, just north of the charming hamlet of Mono Centre. Here, three small outliers known as the Mono Rocks protrude above the glacial fill. Other bedrock exposures can be found in the river valleys, where water has carried away loose deposits. Road cuts also occasionally reach bedrock.

The depth and structure of the Earthen Scarp's buried limestone bedrock has usually been determined by data from well drilling. The records kept by commercial well drillers have been compiled by government agencies, and bedrock maps produced. Here again, a great deal of variation exists in the contours of the bedrock. The combination of irregularity in the bedrock base and in the depth of glacial deposits has produced an extremely varied surface. While the scarp face may have disappeared from sight, the drop in elevation and the vistas it produces are noticeable as you travel from west to east and descend the Escarpment.

The rivers flowing off the Escarpment in this area have an easterly direction, and have carved out a series of valleys that give a very irregular shape to the general line of the Escarpment. These valleys in the face of the rock scarp, or re-entrants, as geologists call them, were present before the time of the glaciers. A stationary ice front paralleled the Escarpment, blocking off the usual valley outlets and redirecting meltwater to the south during the period of glacial melt. This created a number of typically shallow and broad valleys called discharge channels between the rows of moraines. Today they are low-lying areas with more than their share of cedar swamps. The Pleistocene rivers that flowed in these channels carried a great deal of glacial debris. The ancient rivers washed and sorted this material and left large deposits of gravel that are quarried today.

Because of the north-south orientation of the glacial lobe in the region of the Earthen Scarp, both the moraines which it deposited and the channels that drained its meltwaters trend in a similar north-south direction. After the last of the ice melted away, the discharge channels were abandoned, and drainage patterns reverted to the preglacial valleys.

In the townships of Mulmur and Mono a series of rivers with deep, narrow, rugged and forested valleys (especially in their upper reaches) break up the land into a set of east-west trending upland blocks. Only as the rivers exit the upland areas do their valleys become more open and amenable to farming. These rivers, with the exception of the most northerly Pretty River, are all part of the Nottawasaga River system.

It is on top of these upland areas that the bulk of the farmland is found. In the "Scarp of the Valleys," human settlement concentrated in the valleys themselves. Because so much morainic deposition and river erosion has taken place in the valleys of the Earthen Scarp, many of the fields are very steep. These are usually under pasture. At fleeting moments, because of the lay of the land and the nature of the farming practices, I had a feeling of being in the cattle country of Southern Alberta rather than on the Escarpment of Southern Ontario. Another feature of the landscape is the presence of numerous pine plantations (Red Pines are commonly planted) that from a distance have a distinctive dark, block-like appearance.

South of the Hockley Valley, in the Caledon and Albion Hills, the landscape loses some of its open, rugged character. The hills grow gentler, more wooded; and there is a greater sense of enclosure. In the eastern portion of Caledon, in what used to be Albion Township, the Escarpment slope itself peters out, but the hilliness of the landscape is maintained by the Oak Ridges Moraine. Here two ice lobes met, one coming north from Lake Ontario and the other coming south from Lake Simcoe, and between them a huge moraine was piled up.

Like most Escarpment areas, Caledon has it share of swamps. On top of the Escarpment, the scouring action of the ice left large areas with little soil and poor drainage. These swampy sections are especially noticeable during the spring thaw, when some gravel roads that pass through them turn into quagmire and you have to dipsy-doodle your way through gravelly mush.

We are now within easy reach of Toronto and the land is abundantly dotted with rural estates, kilometres of horse fences, and a sense of urban money and gentility that is not found in the high country of Mono and Mulmur. That is not to say that there are no modest dwellings or working farms in this portion of the Escarpment, but merely to say that in some parts of Caledon the money is there and can not only be seen, but at times also felt.

Caledon forms a notable divide. The original land surveys divided the countryside into counties and townships. Townships are divided into concessions and lots that are the basis of land ownership for the farmer. In the predominantly rural areas of the province, this form of geographic organisation is still the the method of choice. City people in Southern Ontario, on the other hand, live in regions, cities and towns. North of Caledon we find only counties and townships along the Escarpment, and from Caledon on South we find that the Escarpment passes through only regions, cities and towns. The political designations reflect the increased urbanisation that has occurred around Lake Ontario.

Interestingly, in the past few years the Town of Caledon, which a number of years ago was created from the union of Caledon and Albion Townships, has renamed its roads. The old farm designation of 3rd Line East, which says a lot to a farmer but means much less to a city person, has been replaced by Horseshoe Hill Road, which sounds more natural to an urban ear. And the 10th Sideroad is now known as Escarpment Sideroad.

Since we find ourselves at Horseshoe Hill Road and Escarpment Sideroad, I may as well digress briefly and mention a train derailment at this location that killed 7 people in 1907. The Toronto, Grey and Bruce Railway had sought a route by which to climb the Escarpment. All the easily and safely climbed routes had been taken by other railroads, or were in the hands of land owners or towns that wanted a king's ransom to allow the rails to come through. The railway company initially had hoped to go through the Humber River gap at Mono Mills, but had to bypass the town. The determined rail builders sought out an alternate route—they would bull their way up a relatively gentle portion of the Caledon Mountain slope using a couple of extremely sharp horseshoe turns to lower the grades to a level that trains could climb. For about 35 years these curves were safely traversed, but eventually a passenger train coming down the Escarpment derailed on one of the sharp turns, with loss of life. Passengers claimed the train was moving much too quickly, but ultimately no legal blame was placed on the engineer. The line was eventually closed because of the excessively steep grades.

Driving around the site of the derailment ninety years later, I could see no sign of the old railbed. But the property on which it occurred displayed a For Sale sign offering development potential. Just above this property, a rather large structure that perhaps only new money could find fully appropriate for the site was in the process of being built. And still within eyesight of the crash, a treed 15-acre lot was being offered at a little over a third of a million.

A bedrock outlier capped by Amabel dolostone, north of Mono Centre. Called the Mono Rocks, there are three of these small outcroppings.

The forested valley of the Boyne River. The sides of the valley are steep and in pasture. The vista to the east is typical of the view from this part of the Escarpment. It is misty just after a shower; more often it is hazy.

Caledon near the Escarpment brow. Agricultural land here has gone out of production. The glacial deposits are often coarse, stony and of limited fertility.

Uplands of Mulmur. This area is just east of the buried brow of the Escarpment. Much of the area has a rugged pastoral look. It is only farther to the east that there is a pronounced drop in elevation and the land becomes dissected.

Albion Hills. A farm on the rolling hills of the Oak Ridges Moraine just east of the Escarpment. Properties such as this usually become estate horse farms for wealthy urbanities if they come on the market.

Hockley Valley. This rugged, picturesque and photogenic valley with its grand vistas at times has a mountainous aura. Like the other major valleys, it was originally eroded by pre-glacial rivers and then widened and deepened by glaciers. A large amount of glacial debris was left behind. The rounded hills in the foreground are examples of this deposition.

A pastoral scene on the earth-covered Escarpment in Mono Township. The zone of Escarpment in Mono and Mulmur townships is several miles wide and at times does not have the traditional Escarpment appearance.

Valley of the Noisy River at Dunedin. The gently rounded hill in the background is the Smith or Ten Hill Outlier. The Ten Hill is unusual in that it lacks the hard caprock which is typical of most outliers. Instead it is topped by the weak shales of the Queenston Formation, which results in its softened appearance. Compare it to the Milton Outlier on Page 96.

Interior of a Red Pine plantation. The plantations in this area are the most stately that I've ever seen.

The planting of evergreen trees is a well-established practice on more rugged and sandy land in Mono and Mulmur.

Albion Hills descending the Escarpment. The countryside, though rolling, is not as open or rugged as the fields of Mono and Mulmur.

Another view of the rugged hills of Mono and Mulmur. We are well to the east of the official line of the buried Escarpment brow. The rugged topography is a combination of irregularities in bedrock and glacial deposits. Note the characteristic soft and round shape of these hills.

Boyne Valley. The valley is heavily forested in its upper reaches. The river has cut into the plateau, leaving many steep-sided fields which are maintained in permanent pasture. The landscape in this part of the Escarpment has a ruggedness to it not typical of most Southern Ontario farmland.

North of Glen Huron. The Escarpment slopes are more gentle and uniform in this scene than in the previous photograph. However, near the top the bedrock is exposed and fields are replaced by woodlots. Note the triangular appearance of the fields. This landscape is quite distinctive, and different from both the Caledon and the Mono-Mulmur looks.

A light early winter snowfall brings out fine detail, providing visual interest on this hilly countryside typical of Mulmur and Mono.

Steep slopes typical of the earth-covered Escarpment.

The Noisy River Valley approaching Glenedin from the south. These hills and vistas were reminiscent of the hills of Scotland to the early settlers from the United Kingdom.

Pine River Valley as it nears the edge of the heavily dissected plateau of the Escarpment. The valley in its lower reaches is broad and arable. The Pine, Boyne and Noisy Valleys are less well-known to urban dwellers of the southern cities since they are farther away, rural, and not covered with ski slopes. There is no clearly-defined scarp face in areas such as this, just a broad zone that is considered to be part of "the Escarpment."

North of Dunedin on the road to Glen Huron. We have just left Dunedin and are climbing the north slope of the Noisy River Valley. Notice the soft and gentle lines of the hills, even though the relief is quite great.

The Violet Hill Discharge Channel. This is a broad flat-bottomed valley that was carved out by glacial meltwater flowing toward the south. Originating just south of the Noisy River Valley (at Lavender), it carried meltwater along the edge of the Escarpment to Orangeville, and emptied into the Credit River system. The low-lying areas are occupied by cedar swamps and pastures. Water in the discharge channels carried and sorted the rubble from the rotting ice. Portions of their valleys contain huge amounts of high quality gravel and are the sites of large gravel pits. These channels are the relic valleys of Pleistocene rivers, and one distinguished and venerable scholar has suggested the Violet Hill Channel be designated "A Pleistocene Heritage River."

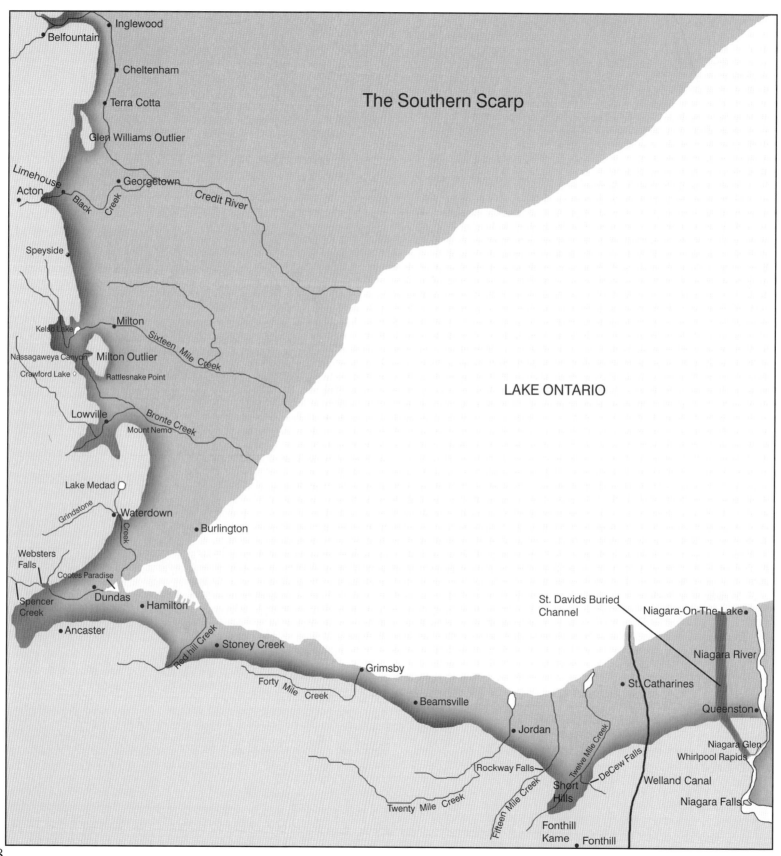

The Southern Scarp

Inglewood

Belfountain

Cheltenham

Terra Cotta

Glen Williams Outlier

Limehouse
Acton

Black Creek

Georgetown

Credit River

Speyside

Milton

Kelso Lake

Sixteen Mile Creek

Nassagaweya Canyon

Milton Outlier

Crawford Lake

Rattlesnake Point

LAKE ONTARIO

Lowville

Bronte Creek

Mount Nemo

Lake Medad

Grindstone

Waterdown

Creek

Burlington

Websters
Falls

Cootes Paradise

Spencer
Creek

Dundas

Hamilton

Ancaster

Red hill Creek

Stoney Creek

St. Davids Buried
Channel

Niagara-On-The-Lake

Niagara River

Grimsby

Forty Mile Creek

Beamsville

St. Catharines

Queenston

Jordan

Twelve Mile Creek

Niagara Glen
Whirlpool Rapids

Rockway Falls

DeCew Falls

Welland Canal

Twenty Mile Creek

Fifteen Mile Creek

Short
Hills

Niagara Falls

Fonthill
Kame

Fonthill

88

THE SOUTHERN SCARP

The Southern Scarp is an urban scarp: it is either part of or within the influence of the urban belt along Lake Ontario. To the north of it is a relatively lightly populated area where vistas are of farm country or bush, and urban intrusion on the countryside is limited. By contrast, in this most southerly region, population density is much greater; cities can often be seen in the distance; and the urban influence is stronger in the countryside. To experience more natural landscapes, you must take greater care in choosing areas of the Escarpment to explore.

The Credit River has left its mark on the Escarpment. Its main branch originates near Orangeville and passes through hummocky and at times swampy land above the Escarpment. It descends the Escarpment at Cataract, while the west branch descends at Belfountain. Its gorge, both above and below the Forks, is deep and quite steep. Past the Gorge, the Credit quietly parallels the foot of the Scarp in a fairly deep valley between Inglewood and the Glen Williams Outlier before veering eastward, away from the Escarpment. Its many small tributaries that drain the earth-covered Scarp face in this area have contributed to the rolling nature of the countryside.

This is the setting where numerous mills once graced the landscape. These have now, by and large, joined those who built and operated them. Each town has its own well-documented stories of individual entrepreneurs who in the mid-1800s built these structures and dreamed the great dream of endless growth. In these quiet and gracious hamlets and towns, many of the old buildings have been artistically restored.

Here also, limestone and sandstone were quarried and the Queenston shale made into bricks. A rail line, now abandoned, climbed the Escarpment via the Credit Gorge. Like Caledon this area is now firmly within the influence of Toronto, and numerous rural estates are found amidst the farms and woodlots. Several ski facilities cling to the more rugged slopes.

The Southern Scarp has the most equal balance between exposed and buried scarp face of all the regions. Quiet areas of scarp face with moderate slopes are typical, alternating with a number of showier steep cliffs. The Escarpment bisects the Town of Halton Hills on a diagonal into an upper and lower half. In places the Escarpment is partially buried and its modest slopes are used for farming and woodlots. It is possible to descend the Escarpment in some locations and not even know it—as I have done on numerous occasions even when aware that I was very close to the brow. The heavily-treed nature of the countryside sometimes obscures the vistas that I so heavily rely upon. Speyside is one such location.

Two of the better known points on the Escarpment are Mount Nemo and Rattlesnake Point—rather prominent promontories separated by the valley of Bronte Creek. Rattlesnake Point is on the Milton Outlier, the best known of the Escarpment outliers. Just to the west is the mysterious and interesting Lake Crawford. It is small and, for its size, deep. The bottom of the lake is undisturbed by water currents or wave action, maintaining its temperature near freezing and the water almost free of oxygen. These conditions preclude organisms that would noticeably disturb the bottom and cause decay. Even the finest of normally short-lived particles, such as pollen grains, can be preserved indefinitely. Such lakes are known as meromictic lakes and are fairly rare.

Each year, separate layers of fine light and dark sediments drift down to the bottom of the lake. The light sediment is composed of calcite (lime) and the dark layer contains organic materials and iron sulphide. This annual accumulation of a light and a dark layer is referred to as a varve. The great value of varves is that they allow very accurate dating of the sediments—in a manner similar to tree ring dating. Each of these layers is flat and thin, and so I imagine each varve to be like a page in a book. But this is a book of 10,000 pages. It is as though Mother Nature were keeping over the millennia an annual diary of matters of interest to herself. You have then, in the lower depths of an unexplained cavity in the Escarpment's bedrock, a cold stagnant body of water that acts like a dead lake. On its bottom lies The Book of Varves—the scientist's equivalent of the Dead Sea scrolls. Such is Lake Crawford.

In itself, this lake would be little more than an interesting geologic oddity titillating the fantasies of geologists. However, our story does not end there. Examining material contained in the varves, scientists discovered fossilised corn pollen grains that were grown between 1350-1650 A.D. This find led to archaeological activity around Lake Crawford and the discovery of a number of well-established Iroquoian village sites.

The main value of the sediments has been to provide a means of accurately dating these sites, which would not be possible in any other way. The examination of varve contents has also provided an insight into the way of life of these old cultures through the discovery of such material as sunflower shells. This kind of information, combined with objects and knowledge from the excavations, has made possible a superb reconstruction of an Iroquoian village at Crawford Lake. It has also provided new knowledge for piecing together the history of the early inhabitants of this continent.

The Dundas Valley probably has more variety per square mile than any other portion of the Niagara Escarpment. Near the Valley's upper end, cut into the north wall, is a steep-sided rock-walled gorge with two branches, each headed by a waterfall. The gorges were created by torrents of glacial meltwater during the glaciers' final throes. When in full flood, Websters Falls—the larger of the two waterfalls—will impress even a Romantic seeking the Deluge. During its quiet summer days, when the living is easy even for a river, the more agile can walk behind its modest flow.

From the canyon of Spencer Gorge one enters the main valley with its gently rolling morainic hills, some relatively untouched by erosion and others deeply dissected. Toward the Valley's mouth a lovely shallow wetland named Cootes Paradise can be seen in the shadow of the Escarpment promontory named Dundas Peak. Within the City of Hamilton the bedrock scarp rises tall above the earthen valley floor as it crosses the city.

It is possible to clamber in isolated gorges listening to the sound of rapids, canoe in the marsh or down a bayou-like stream, go horseback riding amidst gentle hills, or attend Opera Hamilton, all within a 15-minute drive. The Dundas Valley offers a "wilderness" experience for an urban soul like myself who hesitates to wander too far beyond the city. Through an aggressive land acquisition program when government money was plentiful and land still cheap and available, large areas of the Valley were purchased and set aside for public use. This is a side of Hamilton that few people know. Most travellers on the QEW zoom by on the eastern side of the city and see only the grimy behemoths of the steel-making industry.

The Niagara Peninsula below the Escarpment is heavily built-up, and much of this former glacial lake plain has been urbanised. The largest urban areas are Hamilton, Grimsby and St.Catharines; a number of smaller communities fill in the countryside between them. Along with the actual built-up areas, large-scale proliferation of urban dwellings has taken place in the countryside, a result of the extensive land severing that usually takes place near urban centres. The Niagara Peninsula is really just one big sprawling suburb, with little "clean" countryside left.

The scarp from Hamilton to Grimsby is narrow, steep and straightforward. However a little beyond Grimsby, the Escarpment develops a number of terraces or "benches," as they are called locally, that add to the complexity and interest of the landscape. These terraces were created in two different ways. The lowest terrace is the result of wave erosion by glacial Lake Iroquois during glacial meltdown. Water levels in this now defunct lake were higher than the current level of Lake Ontario and produced a typical beach profile of water-washed sands and gravels. Higher, rock-based terraces were formed by the same mechanism encountered in the Wiarton and Owen Sound area: differential erosion, with harder layers of rock forming level plateaux.

In contrast to much of the lake plain below, the terraces for the most part still retain a rural flavour. Orchards are numerous. However, with the renaissance in the wine industry, both areas have been blanketed with vineyards; these have also climbed onto the "Mountain" itself in the effort to keep up with demand.

The quality of Niagara wines has risen greatly, and they are being exported all over the world. One of the most important reasons for this success has been the development of vines capable of producing the quality of grape required. Native North American vines that were resistant to local soil diseases could not produce the necessary quality, and European varieties with the quality could not adapt to local conditions. By grafting the European vivifera scion onto the rootstock of the local labrusca vine, horticulturists succeeded in producing the quality of grape required. With innovative wine-making technologies, Niagara winemasters have achieved the standard they sought.

While the grape-producing area is fairly small, the presence of the Escarpment has created distinct variations in microclimates, soils and drainage, which in turn have led to a certain amount of local specialising in grape species. The terraces or benches in general have better water and air drainage, and winds off the Escarpment break up still frosts, thus providing a little longer growing season than on the lake plain. The low and flat lake plain, on the other hand, has the hotter summer temperatures needed by some species of grape.

The area's natural beauty is enhanced by waterfalls and gorges that have been cut into the Escarpment brow. Some of these were the sites of water-powered mills which have long since gone out of use. I was quite taken by the charm and atmosphere of the mill at DeCew Falls, which is being restored to working condition by a group of volunteers in co-operation with the City of St. Catharines. It was quite an experience to watch the water wheel, now in working condition, and sense the much more leisurely pace of work of the watermill era.

While wandering about the DeCew mill property I was struck by the differences between it and the mill at Walters Falls, on the Escarpment brow at the head of the Bighead Valley in Grey County near Meaford. Here on the outskirts of St.Catharines, the small property is fenced off by neighbouring private homes trying to achieve a little privacy. A sign warns you not to step onto the dam. But the mill building and machinery are being superbly restored by individuals with a real feel for the project.

Walters Falls, on the other hand, is in true rural country and is too remote to attract many tourists. There are no reasons, let alone resources, to restore the structure or equipment. Scattered about the mill site is old rusting machinery still lying where it was dumped after a fire that occurred in the mid-1980s. Some of the dam structure is a little run-down, but you are free to wander about as you choose without any warning signs. There are no fences near the gorge and it is yours to explore. I imagine it is private property, but it did not seem to matter. Two mills: one near a lot of people and one not.

The reader may recall our previous discussions of the great deluges that occurred when the massive mountains of ice melted. We have seen that temporary rivers pouring from the ice hollowed out shallow river valleys called discharge channels. Temporary lakes also formed beside the receding ice. Often, rivers flowing from the rotting ice carried a great deal of earthen debris into the lakes, forming deltas. The water-transported material was sorted, as was material that settled in still lake water. In some cases large deposits of river-washed gravels were laid down, and in others much finer deposits settled underwater.

A large glacial lake delta was created in the area just southwest of St.Catharines known as the Short Hills. After all the ice and water were gone, this flat little terrace was eroded into rolling hills by Twelve Mile Creek. The flat top of the original delta can be distinguished by an observant eye. The intimate dissected terrain of the Short Hills is the site of a provincial park that functions as a nature reserve for St. Catharines. The pretty hill country around Fonthill is similar in origin to the Short Hills. Geologists use the word "kame" to describe glacial landforms composed of layered water-worked materials. These deposits often take on a distinctive steep, irregular conical hill shape.

Water has the power to erode. The more there is and the faster it flows, the more it erodes. The effects of rain water and seepage from layered rock, combined with frost action, have caused the Escarpment face as a whole to retreat over time. Rivers flowing over the Escarpment with greater flows of water have eroded gorges into the main face. The Niagara River, having by far the most volume, has eroded the fastest and farthest. In slightly over 11,000 years it has cut an 11-kilometre long gorge into the scarp. That is very fast. This rate has dramatically slowed with the construction of hydro-electric facilities which divert water that once flowed over the Falls into man-made structures that power the great dynamos. In this respect the bulk of the Niagara River is now going down the tubes.

The Upper Great Lakes, above the Escarpment, have always had to find their way to the sea, doing so by crossing the Niagara Peninsula and draining to the Lower Great Lakes. The path taken across the peninsula has shifted location a number of times. Several gorges carved into the Escarpment by these ancient flows are now buried by glacial debris. Their location has been determined mainly by drilling down to bedrock. The St. David's Buried Gorge carried the flow out from the Whirlpool in the Niagara Gorge. Another buried channel is believed to have flowed through the valley now occupied by the Short Hills.

The Niagara Gorge is unique for its massive rapids, but also in another respect. During the busy season helicopters roar endlessly overhead ferrying tourists above the Falls; a cable car shuttles out regularly, and now and then a commercial power boat roars up to the rapids. Who said that people don't love nature! By the way, if you ever want to experience what Vietnam must have been like during the days of the American military presence, go to the Whirlpool Rapids on a good flying day and listen to and watch the helicopters. It's actually quite impressive and as long as you accept it for what it is, an enjoyable outing can be had. If you wish to enjoy the power and beauty of the Gorge and rapids undisturbed, just go when there are no tourist activities.

The vistas off the Escarpment in the Niagara Peninsula reflect the ubiquitous urban presence. Looking down to the lake plain below, the scenes range from an unbroken sea of rooftops in the vicinity of the cities, to a densely settled rural countryside. Looking out over Lake Ontario, the glitter of the Toronto skyline is visible.

A drive through this area can be just as much a part of the Escarpment experience as standing atop a promontory overlooking Georgian Bay. I use the term 'drive' deliberately. With the high density of rural settlement, paved roads and increased traffic, few roads would be very safe to walk on, and those rare unpaved "Escarpment roads" are mostly to be found in the Short Hills. Numbers of fine trails for walking permit exploration on foot, however, including the Escarpment's faithful companion, the Bruce Trail.

The lands of the Niagara Peninsula are varied, pretty, and have more human artefacts to interest one. It is easy to enjoy the natural beauty of the Escarpment in this area, but you must seek it out in the special places that have been set aside, such as the conservation areas. The rugged gorges and rolling hills are still there, and away from Niagara Falls are as quiet and peaceful as ever. Within their forested confines the rest of the world is as far away as your soul allows it to be.

The Niagara Glen, in the Niagara Gorge. The Niagara Gorge is easily accessible to the public at a number of places, such as the Glen and the Whirlpool. Many huge rocks, some the size of a two-storey house, are scattered throughout the Glen. But for me the most intriguing aspect of the Glen is its resemblance in places to the limestone landscapes portrayed in ink brush paintings by numbers of early Chinese painters.

The gorge of Spencer Creek, Dundas Valley, during an early autumn snowfall. The volume of water coming over the falls was greater than usual.

Dundas Peak in the distance overlooks the entrance to Spencer Gorge. The relatively gentle gradient of the floor of the Dundas Valley provides a natural ramp for the railway to climb the Escarpment wall. A small section of straight railbed can be seen in the photograph.

The Milton Outlier from Mt. Nemo. In the upper left where the land meets the sky, the shadowy bowl-shaped outline of the Nassagaweya Canyon separates the Milton Outlier from the main body of the Escarpment. The rocky bluff of Rattlesnake Point is visible in the centre, and to the right the Scarp's tell-tale outline can be seen as it turns away. This outlier is quite flat due to its hard Lockport dolostone caprock. Look back to page 75 and notice how rounded the shale-covered outlier at Ten Hill is by comparison.

The Short Hills on the outskirts of St. Catharines. Here a glacial delta composed mostly of fine silt has been highly dissected by Twelve Mile Creek and its tributaries, producing a series of rugged hills. Like the Dundas Valley, it is located in a notch in the Escarpment. It is now a provincial park.

Vines and orchard on a plateau, or bench of the Escarpment in the Niagara Peninsula. Slightly past Grimsby the Escarpment becomes more varied on its journey to the Niagara Gorge. Benches such as this one are found in the Jordan and Beamsville area. Being farther away from the big cities and the major freeway passing through the Peninsula, they are more rural in character.

Orchard on the glacial lake plain near Grimsby. In the area between Hamilton and Grimsby, the Escarpment rises abruptly and steeply from the lake plain, and is clearly defined. Here the expression "the thin green line" is most descriptive.

The valley of Fifteen Mile Creek at Rockway Falls. Several Escarpment rivers and their valleys in the Niagara Peninsula are places of rugged and peaceful natural beauty close to large cities—in this case, St.Catharines.

Rattlesnake Point on the Milton Outlier.

Backlit trees in a river gorge. This is one of the most common sights when trekking on the Bruce Trail during the summer. At the bottom of the picture the river can be seen. The rock at the bottom is the reddish Queenston shale, and above it the grey limestones are found. The tree leaves are those of the ubiquitous sugar maple.

The gorge of Fifteen Mile Creek at Rockway Falls. I have never seen any pictures of this lovely little canyon cut deeply into the rock. This photograph and the two that follow give some idea of its beauty.

Rockway Falls. The Lower Falls provides an example of differential erosion of layered limestone. The layering has resulted in a beautiful series of semi-circular steps: an aquatic amphitheatre. Look closely at the picture on page 100 and you will see, from above, the rock ledges in this photograph.

The base of the Upper Falls at Rockway. Timeless rhythms of water and rock exert a powerful attraction.

Glacial landforms at twilight in the Upper Dundas Valley.

he Upper Dundas Valley during a winter windstorm. The dolostone cliffs at the head of the Valley have long since been buried by glacial debris, and now only the soft and beautiful hills of the glacial cover are visible. When you live in an area, it is relatively easy to capture special moments of nature's beauty such as this dust storm.

This field owned by a conservation authority is being allowed to revert back to woodland. Conservation authorities often feel that a field isn't being properly conserved unless it is forested. The prevailing ethic is that you can have mowed lawn or fully wooded areas but not much in between. They could have been Henry Ford's colour consultants when he built his first cars. Leaving unusually picturesque landforms in grassland or savannah is something worthy of discussion, but in practice seldom done. Walking in fields of waving grass and wildflowers and enjoying the undulations of the land unobstructed by trees is seemingly not quite as good a nature experience as walking under the boughs of trees. Diversity of habitat is solemnly proclaimed to be a virtue worth striving for: but funding, you know. That's the problem. In an age of financial constraint, what million-dollar operation can afford to mow a hundred acres once every few years to keep the young tree whips down.

The Bruce Trail passes a long-abandoned apple orchard that has been colonised by hawthorn trees.

A small marsh, part of the Credit River system, helps to separate the Glen Williams Outlier from the main scarp, which is to the left. We are a little north of Georgetown, close to the Silver Creek Conservation Area.

A misty morning in spring. Rolling hills merge with the Scarp, seen two miles in the distance across the Dundas Valley.

Field of grape vines at the upper edge of the Escarpment in the Niagara Peninsula. The wine industry has expanded greatly in the last several years with the development of high-quality grape vines.

Orchards in the intimate rolling countryside of the Fonthill kame. These hills have geological origins similar to the Short Hills a little to the north.

DeCew Falls. This waterfall is in suburban St. Catharines. One inch to the left of this photograph of a natural landscape is the foundation of a restored grist mill with a genuine operating water wheel. A delight for boys of all ages.

A talus slope typical of large areas of the exposed Southern Scarp. The grade is relatively gentle; there is some earth cover; moss grows over the jumble of rocks; rotting trunks add strong diagonal lines; and a small stream bed courses through the composition.

Sulphur Creek meanders through a deep valley cut in the fine silts of the Dundas Valley.

This lovely little hill, only metres away from where the Escarpment emerges as a rocky outcropping, is typical of how glacial deposits covered much of the Escarpment.

Another view of the hills of the Dundas Valley. Here the sun is shining in part of the Valley while a late autumn snow squall passes in the distance.

Cootes Paradise, with Dundas peak in the distance. At one time the open water of this wetland in the Dundas Valley was covered with cattail marsh vegetation. Carp has been the principle agent for the loss of vegetation. An introduced species to North America, this fish has a feeding habit that is destructive to aquatic vegetation: while grubbing for food in the soft marsh mud, it uproots the weakly-anchored plants. Four decades after the the marsh was demolished, a device recently put into place now prevents carp from entering the wetland, and some of the open water in this picture should be replaced by marsh vegetation before too many years have passed. The water in much of this picture is quite shallow; an adult can walk across in most places and not get his head wet.

Earth-covered scarpland lit by low afternoon sun.